ZOO ANIMALS

This Edition first published 2002 by
MENTOR BOOKS
43 Furze Road • Sandyford Industrial Estate • Dublin 18.
Tel. (01) 295 2112/3 • Fax. (01) 295 2114
e-mail: admin@mentorbooks.ie • www.mentorbooks.ie

ISBN: 1-84210-141-2

Design and layout by Kathryn McKinney
Printed in Ireland by ColourBooks

Animal heads come in many shapes.

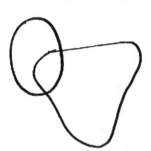

Egg and triangle

Pelican

Big circle and
small circle

Wolf

DRAWING ZOO ANIMAL HEADS

Horizontal line

Vertical line

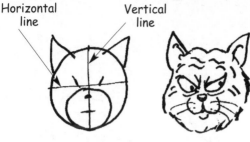

Big circle and small circle

Wildcat

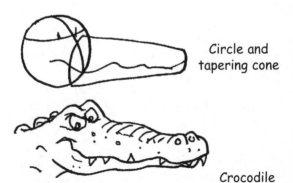

Circle and tapering cone

Crocodile

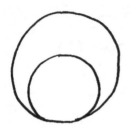

Begin with two circles.

Always put in guide lines with a pencil.

Draw in eyes, nose, mouth and ears.

Add final detail.

ZIGGY ZEBRA

1. Start with a pencil to work out the shapes.

2. Add more detail.

3. Finish with a felt-tip marker. Rub out all your pencil lines.

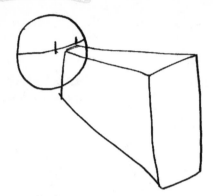

1 & 2. Start with a pencil to work out the shapes.

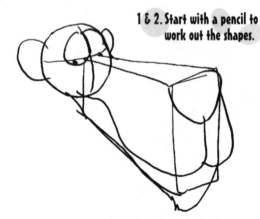

LAZY LION

3. Add more detail.

Always try to give character to a face.

4. Finish with a felt-tip marker. Rub out all your pencil lines.

1. Start with a pencil to work out the shapes.

2. Add more detail.

3. Finish with a felt-tip marker. Rub out all your pencil lines.

1. Start with a pencil to work out the shapes.

2. Add more detail.

3. Finish with a felt-tip marker. Rub out all your pencil lines.

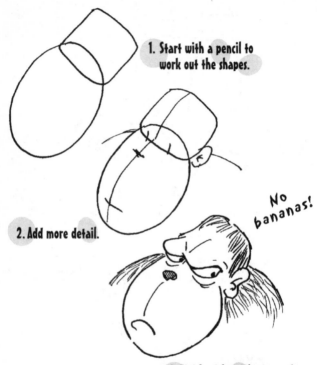

1. Start with a pencil to work out the shapes.

2. Add more detail.

No bananas!

3. Finish with a felt-tip marker. Rub out all your pencil lines.

LET'S DRAW A GORILLA - THE BODY

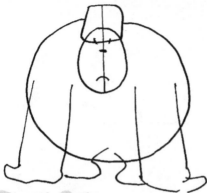

1. Start with a pencil to work out the shapes.

2. Finish with a felt-tip marker. Rub out all your pencil lines.

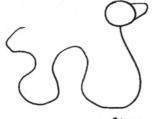

1. Start with a pencil to work out the shapes.

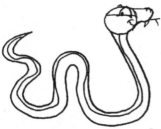

2. Add more detail.

3. Finish with a felt-tip marker. Rub out all your pencil lines.

Action lines suggest movement.

PETE THE PENGUIN

1 & 2. Start with a pencil to work out the shapes.

3. Add more detail.

4. Finish with a felt-tip marker. Rub out all your pencil lines.

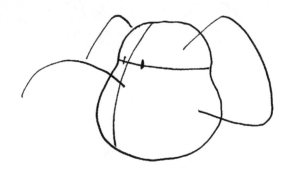

1 & 2. Start with a pencil to work out the shapes.

ELFIE ELEPHANT — THE HEAD

3. Add more detail.

4. Finish with a felt-tip marker.
Rub out all your pencil lines.

*Did somebody
mention peanuts?*

1 & 2. Start with a pencil to work out the shapes.

ELFIE ELEPHANT — THE BODY

3. Add more detail.

**4. Finish with a felt-tip marker.
Rub out all your pencil lines.**

*Notice how action lines
suggest movement.*

1 & 2. Start with a pencil to work out the shapes.

Ha, ha!
Ho, ho!

3. Add more detail.

4. Finish with a felt-tip marker. Rub out all your pencil lines.

PESKY PYTHON

1. Start with a pencil to work out the shapes.

2. Finish with a felt-tip marker. Rub out all your pencil lines.

Sssssssssss!

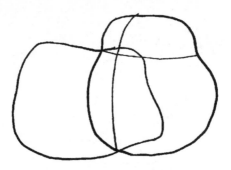

1 & 2. Start with a pencil to work out the shapes.

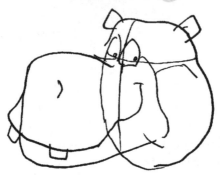

3. Add more detail.

Notice how Jerry's smile affects the shape of his eyes.

4. Finish with a felt-tip marker. Rub out all your pencil lines.

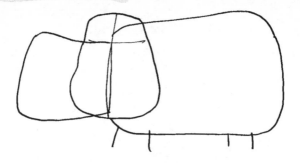

1 & 2. Start with a pencil to work out the shapes.

This early stage is good when you want to make changes. See how the closed mouth is changed to an open mouth.

JERRY THE JOLLY HIPPO – THE BODY

3. Add more detail.

Fancy a mud bath?

4. Finish with a felt-tip marker.
Rub out all your pencil lines.

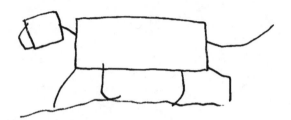

1 & 2. Start with a pencil to
work out the shapes.

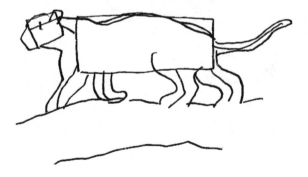

LARRY THE LEOPARD

3. Add more detail.

DO NOT FEED
THE ANIMALS

4. Finish with a felt-tip marker.
Rub out all your pencil lines.

1 & 2. Start with a pencil to work out the shapes.

VERNON VULTURE

3. Add more detail.

4. Finish with a felt-tip marker. Rub out all your pencil lines.

Vernon's looking for a tasty titbit!

1 & 2. Start with a pencil to work out the shapes.

3. Add more detail.

**4. Finish with a felt-tip marker.
Rub out all your pencil lines.**

1 & 2. Start with a pencil to work out the shapes.

SAMUEL SEA LION

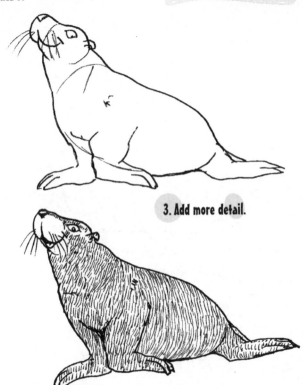

3. Add more detail.

4. Finish with a felt-tip marker. Rub out all your pencil lines.

It's suppertime and Samuel smells his fish!

HAVE FUN!